Today is Divali! It's a special day.

At Divali we light little oil lamps called divas. My diva makes me think about the story of Rama and Sita and how Rama killed Ravana, the demon with ten heads.

I'll tell you the story.

1

Rama and Sita lived in a hut in the forest with Rama's brother, Lakshmana.

"Look, Rama, a deer!" cried Sita one day. "Please catch it for me." Rama ran off into the forest.

After some time, Sita and Lakshmana thought they heard Rama calling, "Lakshmana, please help me."

Lakshmana drew a circle around the hut with his bow. He told Sita, "Stay close to the hut and you'll be safe."

3

Sita was left alone. Then Ravana, the demon with ten heads, came to the hut. He was dressed like a holy man so Sita did not know it was Ravana.

"Please give me some food," he begged Sita.

Sita brought Ravana some food. As she came close, Ravana grabbed her and carried her off in his flying chariot.

He took her to his home in Lanka.

Jatayu, the great bird, tried to help Sita, but Ravana cut Jatayu's wing with his sword. Jatayu fell to the ground.

Rama and Lakshmana returned to the hut. They saw that Sita was missing and were very upset.

"I'll help you to find Sita," said Hanuman, the leader of the monkeys.

He found her in Lanka, but Ravana would not let Sita go free.

Hanuman asked all the monkeys and the other animals in the forest to join his army. They all agreed.

Rama, Lakshmana, Hanuman and the army of animals travelled to Lanka.

Ravana was waiting for them. He was ready with his army! He laughed at Rama.

"Look at Rama with an army of animals," he cried!

9

There were many battles. Ravana the demon was very strong. Lakshmana was wounded.

Then Rama put a special arrow in his bow. He shot the arrow at Ravana. Ravana fell down dead.

Everyone was happy! Rama had killed the demon Ravana!

At last, Rama found Sita again. They went home together.

Everyone was pleased to see Rama and Sita. They lit little diva lamps and came into the streets to light the way for Rama and Sita.

"Welcome home, Rama and Sita," they cried.

We have cleaned the house and sent Divali cards. This afternoon we will have a party.

My sisters and I have made rangoli patterns to welcome our friends. There will be special food and sweets to eat.

Our divas are lit and tonight there will be fireworks to remember Rama's success!

Today really is a special day!

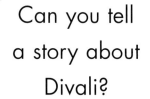

Can you tell a story about Divali?

Published by Religious and Moral Education Press, A division of SCM-Canterbury Press Ltd, St Mary's Works, St Mary's Plain, Norwich, Norfolk NR3 3BH

Copyright © 1999 Lynne Broadbent and John Logan. Lynne Broadbent and John Logan have asserted their right under the Copyright, Designs and Patents Act, 1988, to be identified as Authors of this Work.

All rights reserved. First published 1999. ISBN 1 85175 183 1

Designed and typeset by Topics – The Creative Partnership, Exeter. Printed in Great Britain by Brightsea Press, Exeter for SCM-Canterbury Press Ltd, Norwich